The Cow Jumped Over the ABC's

by Jodi Scheve
illustrated by Kara Barnard

YPC Publishing · Indianapolis

One day lived a cow, and oh did he love to jump.
He practiced night and day, day and night,
jumping a bit higher each day. Until one day
he decided to take on the grand feat of
jumping over all the letters in the alphabet...
and so it begins.

The Cow jumped over
the amusing alligator

The Cow jumped over
the brown boxer

The Cow jumped over
the calm camel

The Cow jumped over
the darling duck

The Cow jumped over
the enormous elephant

The Cow jumped over
the fearless fox

The Cow jumped over
the giant gecko

The Cow jumped over
the hairy hyena

The Cow jumped over
the itchy iguana

The Cow jumped over
the juvenile jaguar

The Cow jumped over
the kindhearted kangaroo

The Cow jumped over
the lounging leopard

The Cow jumped over
the muscular moose

The Cow jumped over
the noble nighthawk

The Cow jumped over
the observant octopus

The Cow jumped over
the poised peacock

The Cow jumped over
the quirky quail

**The Cow jumped over
the rambunctious rabbit**

The Cow jumped over
the slender snake

**The Cow jumped over
the timid tiger**

The Cow jumped over
the uppity umbrella bird

The Cow jumped over the vocal vulture

The Cow jumped over
the worn out warthog

The Cow jumped over
the xanthic x-ray tetra

The Cow jumped over
the young yak

The Cow jumped over the zazzy zebra

The sun was now setting and the cow
realized he had been jumping all day.
Oh, what an accomplishment.
All of the cow's hard work had paid off,
he had jumped over all the
letters of the alphabet.

ISBN 978-1-62890-1

$10.00 U.S.